The Magic Shop

Contents

FULL FLIGHT ✦ runway

Titles in the Runway series

Badger Publishing Limited
15 Wedgwood Gate, Pin Green Industrial Estate,
Stevenage, Hertfordshire SG1 4SU
Telephone: 01438 356907. Fax: 01438 747015
www.badger-publishing.co.uk
enquiries@badger-publishing.co.uk

The Magic Shop ISBN 978 1 84691 369 3

Publisher: David Jamieson
Commissioning Editor: Carrie Lewis
Design: Fiona Grant
Illustration: Oliver Lake, Robin Lawrie, Anthony Williams
Printed and bound in China through Colorcraft Ltd., Hong Kong

>>The Magic Shop

Written by Keith West
Illustrated by Oliver Lake

Paul and Mia saw a magic shop.
"Let's go in," said Paul.

There were strange things in the shop.
There were old bottles and boxes.

There was an old man in the shop.
"Have you got any magic tricks?" said Paul.

"Come with me," said the old man.
"This is a magic box."

"Step inside," said the old man.
Paul stepped inside.

"Paul, don't!" said Mia.

The old man closed the door.

"Open the door!" said Mia.

The old man opened the door.

There was no one in the box.

"Where is Paul?" said Mia.

"Who is he?" said the old man. "You are the only one here."

Stolen Goods

Written by Jillian Powell
Illustrated by Robin Lawrie

The boys went into a sweet shop.
They took some sweets and ran away.

They went into a supermarket.
They took some CDs.

The shop alarm went off.
The boys ran away.

"Look at those boxes. They look like MP3 players."

The boys took the boxes and ran away.

Internet Alert

Written by Stan Cullimore
Illustrated by Anthony Williams

Nick and Rob were on the XBox.

"I wish we had some money to buy a new game," said Nick.

"I can get some money," said Rob.
"I can get a credit card number from the Internet."

They used the credit card number to buy a new game.

The next day the game came.
Nick and Rob played it all day.

Then they went on the Internet.
There was an Internet Alert.

"You used a stolen credit card to buy a game. We will tell the police."

"Now we are in big trouble," said Rob.

▶〉〉 Vocabulary ___

The Magic Shop

magic
shop
bottles
boxes
strange
tricks
step
inside

Stolen Goods

sweet
shop
easy
something
bigger
supermarket
alarm
CDs
MP3 players
trouble
find
car trackers
spies
follow

Internet Alert

Xbox
money
game
credit card number
Internet
buy
alert
trouble

⬤〉〉〉 Story questions ⎯

The Magic Shop

Who worked in the shop?
What did Paul step into?
What should Mia do next?

Stolen Goods

What did the boys steal first?
Where did the boys take the CDs from?
How did the policemen find the boys?

Internet Alert

Why does Nick want more money?
How do the boys get the credit card number?
How were the boys caught?